THE COMPLETE PIANO
BALLADS

Wise Publications
London / New York / Sydney / Paris / Copenhagen / Madrid / Tokyo

Exclusive Distributors:
Music Sales Limited
8/9 Frith Street,London W1V 5TZ, England.
Music Sales Pty Limited
120 Rothschild Avenue, Rosebery, NSW 2018, Australia.

Order No. AM963930
ISBN 0-7119-8158-2
This book © Copyright 1991, 2000 by Wise Publications
(Previously available as *The Complete Piano Player: Easy Listening*)

Compiled by Peter Evans
Music arranged by Kenneth Baker
Music processed by Musicprint
Designed by Pearce Marchbank Studio
Printed in Great Britain by Printwise (Haverhill) Limited, Suffolk.

Your Guarantee of Quality
As publishers, we strive to produce every book to the
highest commercial standards.
The music has been freshly engraved and the book has been
carefully designed to minimise awkward page turns and to
make playing from it a real pleasure.
Particular care has been given to specifying acid-free, neutral-sized
paper made from pulps which have not been elemental chlorine bleached.
This pulp is from farmed sustainable forests and was produced with
special regard for the environment.
Throughout, the printing and binding have been planned to ensure a sturdy,
attractive publication which should give years of enjoyment.
If your copy fails to meet our high standards, please
inform us and we will gladly replace it.

Music Sales' complete catalogue describes thousands of titles and is
available in full colour sections by subject, direct from Music Sales Limited.
Please state your areas of interest and send a cheque/postal order for £1.50 for postage to:
Music Sales Limited, Newmarket Road, Bury St. Edmunds, Suffolk IP33 3YB.

www.musicsales.com

SOMETIMES WHEN WE TOUCH

Words & Music by Dan Hill & Barry Mann.

UNCHAINED MELODY

Music by Alex North. Words by Hy Zaret.

7

THE FIRST TIME EVER I SAW YOUR FACE

Words & Music by Ewan MacColl.

9

PORTRAIT OF MY LOVE

Words by David West. Music by Cyril Ornadel.

I'LL KNOW

Words & Music by Frank Loesser.

KILLING ME SOFTLY WITH HIS SONG

Words by Norman Gimbel. Music by Charles Fox.

LOVE'S BEEN GOOD TO ME

Words & Music by Rod McKuen.

Tenderly ♩ = 69

CHORUS

I have been a ro-ver, I have walked a-lone. Hiked a hun-dred high-ways, ne-ver found a home. Still, in all, I'm hap-py, the rea-son is, you see,

WHAT THE WORLD NEEDS NOW IS LOVE

Words by Hal David. Music by Burt Bacharach.

TOO YOUNG

Words by Sylvia Dee. Music Sid Lippman.

F D7 G7 C9 F13
can't be - gin to know the mean - ing of. And
cresc. f mf
Bb Dm Gm Cm7 F13
yet we're not too young to know this
Bbmaj7 Bb7 Bb7+ Eb
love will last, tho' years may go. And
cresc. f
Cm Ab7 Bb B°
then, some - day they may re - call we were
dim.
Cm F7 Ebm6 Bbadd9
not too young at all.

WHEN YOU'RE YOUNG AND IN LOVE

Words & Music by Van McCoy.

LAY, LADY, LAY

Words & Music by Bob Dylan.

THE LOOK OF LOVE

Words by Hal David. Music by Burt Bacharach.

TRY A LITTLE TENDERNESS

Words & Music by Harry Woods, Jimmy Campbell & Reg Connelly.

WITHOUT YOU

Words & Music by Peter Ham & Tom Evans.

WONDERFUL TONIGHT

Words & Music by Eric Clapton.

MORE THAN I CAN SAY

Words & Music by Sonny Curtis & Jerry Allison.

I'LL BE YOUR LOVER, TOO

Words & Music by Van Morrison.

37

IF NOT FOR YOU

Words & Music by Bob Dylan.

39

THE POWER OF LOVE

Words & Music by C. deRouge, G. Mende, J. Rush & S. Applegate.

IT'S IMPOSSIBLE (SOMOS NOVIOS)

Words by Sid Wayne. Music by A. Manzanero.

ALWAYS ON MY MIND

Words & Music by Wayne Thompson, Mark James & Johnny Christopher.

MY KIND OF GIRL

Words & Music by Leslie Bricusse.

INTERLUDE